It Makes You Think!

Mathematical Puzzles and Problems

Association of Teachers of Mathematics

Published in 2007 by
Association of Teachers of Mathematics
Unit 7 Prime Industrial Park,
Shaftesbury Street
Derby DE23 8YB

Telephone 01332 346599
Fax 01332 204357
E-mail: **admin@atm.org.uk**

© Jill Mansergh 2007

Printed in England

ISBN 978-1-898611-48-6

Copies may be purchased from the above address or **www.atm.org.uk**

Acknowledgments
My thanks to the children and teachers from the following schools in North Somerset for trying out the ideas
in the classroom:

Dundry Primary School	High Down Junior School	Uphill Primary School
Winford Primary School	Wrington Primary School	Yeo Moor Junior School

Particular thanks also to Helen Howe, Maria Petherick Moss, Ann Skelhorne, Ruti Simon and Kate Sparks
for giving very detailed feedback on the activities.

CONTENTS

INTRODUCTION

It Makes You Think is divided into four sections each containing activities designed to develop children's thinking. The activities cover the whole primary range from Reception to Year 6, with some activities also being suitable for lower key stage 3. All the activities have been trialled in schools in North Somerset and Bath & North East Somerset. Feedback from the teachers has been very positive and adjustments have been made to the activities as a result.

This book contains a number of photocopiable pages and all the resources needed for the activities can be printed from the accompanying CD-ROM.

Section 1: Shaping Up

Shaping Up has five different sets of cards. Colour plays a significant part in the use of these cards, which can be reproduced from the files on the CD-ROM. Several sorting activities and games are suggested for the cards. They can also provide a starting point for investigations.

Section 2: Colour Sudoku

Colour Sudoku allows children from the foundation stage upwards to engage with reasoning and logic. The use of the boards on the CD-ROM enables children to use cubes rather than pencil and paper to complete the puzzles.

Section 3: Plonka Boards

Plonka Boards provide a different way for children to give answers in mental and oral starters or the main part of a lesson. In response to questions children either put a counter on the answer or plonk their finger on the solution – hence the name. The boards can be photocopied onto paper, or card, if they are to be used regularly.

Section 4: Clued up

Clued Up is a series of collaborative problem solving activities. All the resources needed for the activities are on the CD-ROM. The activities aim to develop both individual and group problem solving skills in interesting and meaningful contexts.

SECTION 1: SHAPING UP

Shaping Up has five different sets of cards. These examples give an idea of what each set of cards is like. Colour plays a significant part in the use of the cards and they can be reproduced in colour from the accompanying CD-ROM.

Set 1 has 27 cards with one shape on each card. The shapes are square, circle and triangle in red, yellow and blue. They are in three sizes, small, medium and large.

Set 2 has 27 cards each showing two shapes in red yellow or blue. The shapes are square, circle and triangle, and they are all the same size.

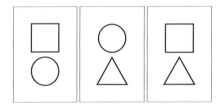

Set 3 has 54 cards each showing two shapes in red, yellow or blue. The shapes are square, circle, triangle and rectangle.

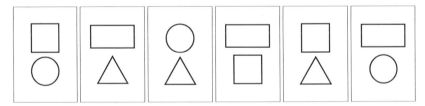

Set 4 has 9 cards each with four coloured shapes. Each card has a circle, a cross and two squares one of which has its sides parallel to an edge of the card and the other with diagonals parallel to the edge. There is a red shape, a blue shape, a yellow shape and a green shape on each card.

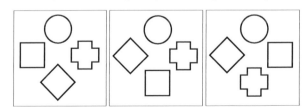

Set 5 has 16 cards which are similar in design to those in set 4.

Thinking activities using the shape cards

The following activities can be used with a set (or part set) of cards appropriate for the level of the children.

Show me questions

Set 1

One attribute
- A red shape
- A shape with three sides
- A shape with curved sides
- A shape which is called a rectangle

More than one attribute
- A shape which is round and red
- A green rectangle
- A small blue shape
- A small red triangle

'Not' questions.
- A shape which is not red
- A shape which is not round
- A shape which is not a rectangle
- A shape which is neither small nor round
- A shape which is neither red nor triangular

Sets 2 and 3

Some of these questions have more than one card for a solution. Ask children find another card to match the criteria? … and another? How many cards would fit the criteria?
- A card which has only red shapes
- A card with red and blue shapes
- A card with only triangles
- A card with a square and a triangle
- A card which has a red circle
- A card with a green square
- A card with a green square and a red shape
- A card with a green square and a circle
- A card with two squares
- A card with two shapes that are the same
- A card shapes that have only straight sides

'Not' questions.

- A card which does not have a circle
- A card which does not have a red shape
- A card which does not have two shapes that are the same colour
- A card which does not have two shapes which are the same shape
- A card which does not have two shapes that have straight sides

This activity can lead on to children placing cards on Carroll Diagrams.

Activities using any of the sets of cards

Sorting Activities

Encourage children to work in pairs or small groups and to sort the cards using criteria of their own choice. Year 1 and 2 children will be able to find a number of different ways to sort the cards. It is a good idea for one of the pair to look at the ways in which other pairs have sorted their cards, leaving their partner to explain to other children how they have organised their cards. Children then swap roles. Selected children may be encouraged to describe their sorting activities to the rest of the class.

The same and different

Take any two shape cards.
What is the same about the shapes?
What is different about them?

This leads on to the next activity.

Find the odd one out

Take any three shape cards. Children decide which the odd one out of the three cards is and give a reason for their answer. They will manage to make each card the odd one out with sufficient practice.

Card Chains

With Set 1 children make chains changing just one thing with each card. This could be the shape, the colour or the size. Children try to make different lengths of chain that join up to the first card. Challenge children to make the longest possible chain. Ask if it is possible to make a chain using all the cards?

Dominoes

With Sets 2 and 3 children can play dominoes in the usual way.
The rules might be altered by negotiation so that two shapes that are the same but different colours might be touching, or two colours with different shapes can touch.

Domino Chains

Children try to make a domino chain. Cards can be joined if the shapes have just one difference – this may be colour or shape. For example a chain might be: red triangle, red circle, green circle, blue circle, blue square, blue triangle and back to red triangle.

Children try to make a chain that goes back to the starting point.
What is the longest chain you can make?
The shortest chain?
 Can you make a chain of 6 cards?

With sets 2 and 3 the chains become more interesting.
Children can invent rules for games to be played.

Is it possible to make a domino chain using all the cards in Set 2 or Set 3?

Pelmanism

A set of cards is placed face down on the table. Children turn two cards over and if they can find something similar about them (colour, size or shape), they may keep the cards.

A variation that is not so reliant on memory is to turn half the cards face upwards. Children turn over one of the face down cards and find one that is face up which has something similar.

Snap

Children negotiate the rules for snap. This could be that the shapes need to have one, or even two, things in common.

Make up your own game

Encourage children to devise their own games, negotiating the rules with a partner.

Activities for Sets 4 and 5

All the previous activities can be done with Sets 4 and 5 with the exception of the 'Show me' questions. The following activity will require persistence or luck for children to solve.

Squares

The cards in Set 4 can be arranged in a 3 x 3 square so that the sides which touch have the same shape and the same colour. One solution is given – is this a unique solution?

The cards in Set 5 can be arranged to form a 4 x 4 square.

Children can design their own cards to carry out similar activities.

Starting points for investigation

Set 2 has 27 cards. Arrange the cards and convince a partner that all possible combinations have been included.

Make the problem simpler – just use the cards in Set 2 that have red or yellow or both colours. How many are there in this set? Can you show that all the possible combinations have been included?

Is there another way we could make the problem simpler? (e.g. leave out all the cards with a circle)

If in Set 2 the rules are changed so that a card has two triangles, what would the complete set of cards contain?

In Sets 4 and 5 the shapes appear to be randomly placed and coloured. Find different ways of arranging the shapes on the card. Keeping the rule that each card must have four different colours and four different shapes, find possible cards for this set.

There are blank sheets on pages 9 - 16 to support these activities. They can also be printed out from the CD-ROM.

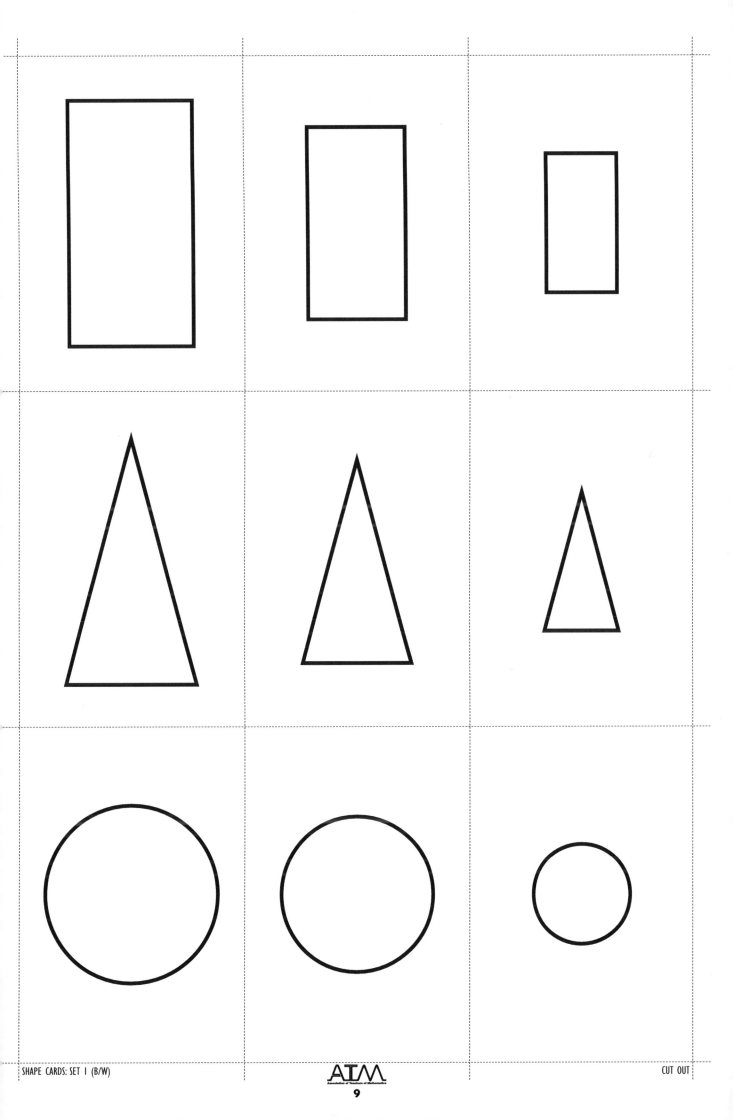

ATM
Association of Teachers of Mathematics

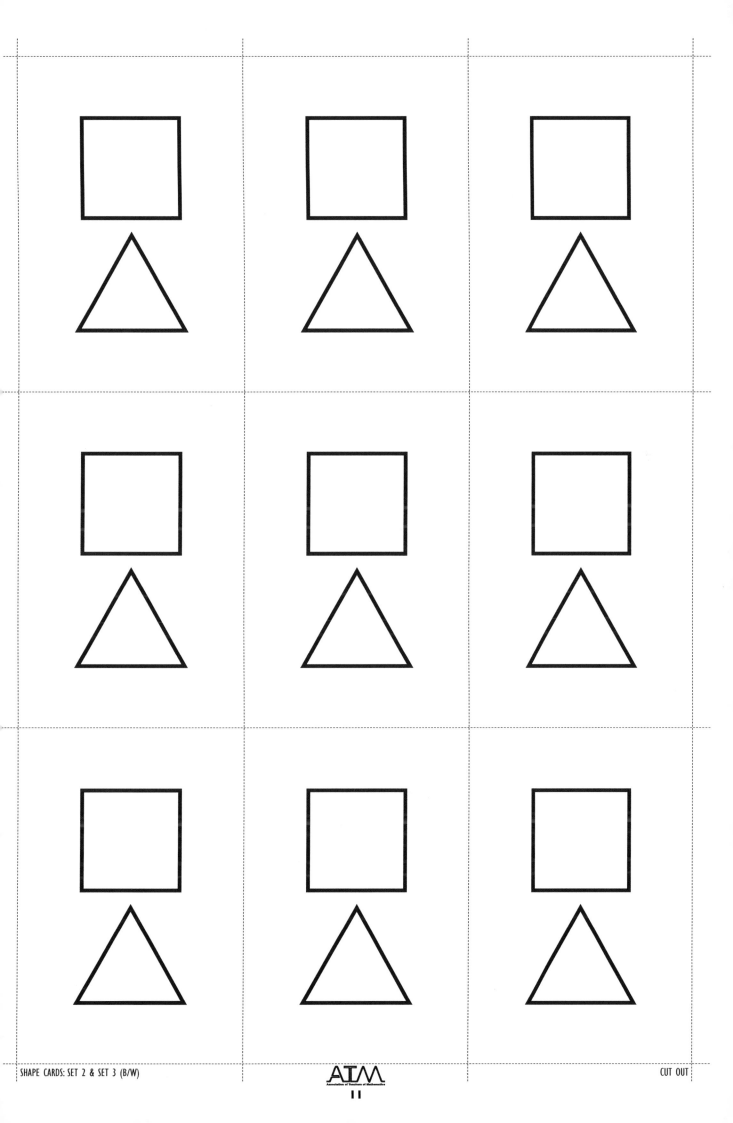

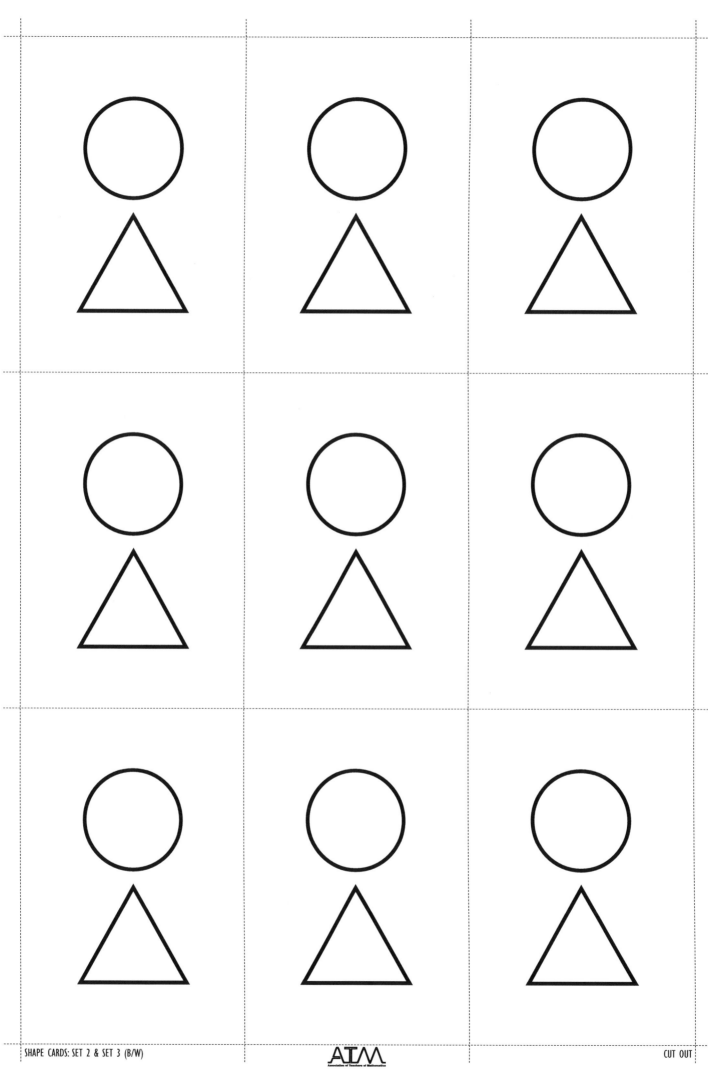

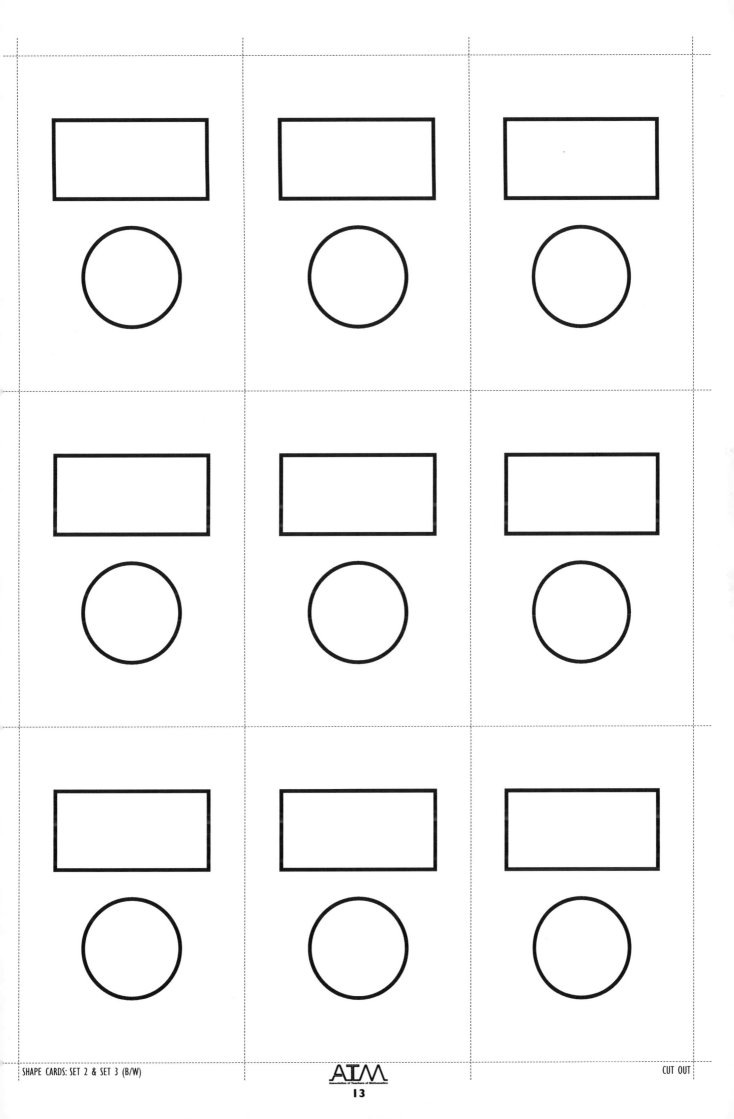

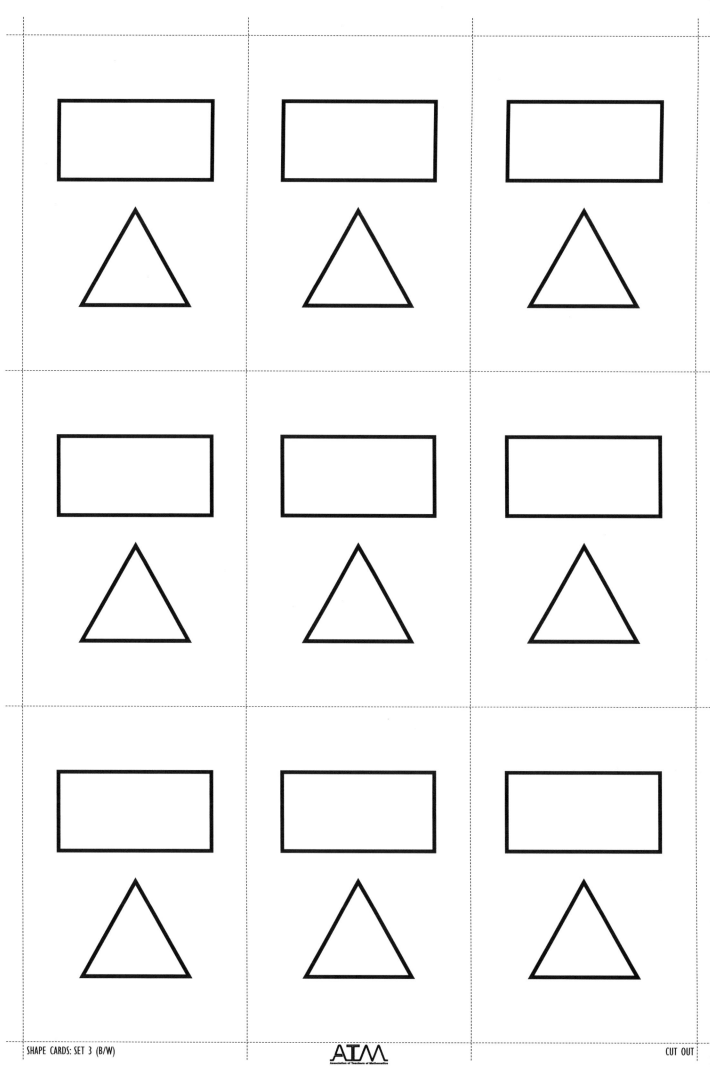

ATM
Association of Teachers of Mathematics

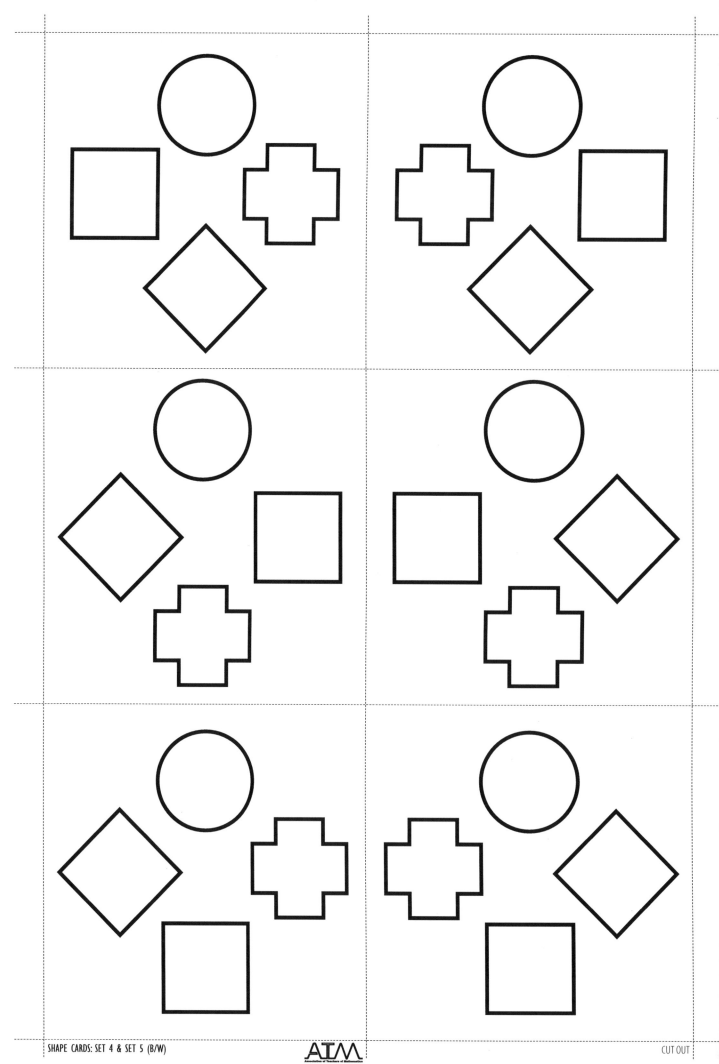

CUT OUT

SECTION 2: COLOUR SUDOKU

Helping children with logical reasoning

Children can express their reasoning using Sudoku. This can be successfully introduced by using 'people' Sudoku. Sixteen chairs are placed in a grid format to represent the board and four children wearing coloured hats represent the coloured cells.

Explain that each colour will appear once in every row, column and mini-grid of four squares. Ask children to look at the grid and if they can see a chair that must be a certain colour then to explain their reasoning. If they are correct they sit in that chair with the appropriate colour hat and the reasoning continues.

It is important to model clear reasoning for the children. One way of doing this is shown in the example. First explain that rows go across the page and columns go up and down. (Letters have been used here to represent the colours Red, Yellow, Green, and Blue.)

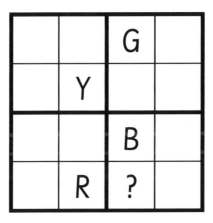

This ? must be yellow

- I know there must be a yellow in that column.
- There is only one other square in that column where it could go.
- Yellow cannot go in that square because there is already a yellow in that row.

This ? must be red

		G	
	Y	?	
		B	
	R	Y	

- I know there must be a red in that column.
- There is only one empty square in that column, so it must be red.

This ? must be yellow

		G	?
	Y	R	
		B	
	R	Y	

- I know there must be a yellow in that mini-grid.
- There are only two squares available in that mini-grid.
- The other square can't be yellow because there is already a yellow in that row.

This ? must be blue

		G	Y
	Y	R	?
		B	
	R	Y	

- It is the only square left in the mini-grid and the mini-grid must contain a blue.

This ? must be green

		G	Y
?	Y	R	B
		B	
	R	Y	

- It is the only square left in the row and the row must contain a green.

This ? must be blue

	?	G	Y
G	Y	R	B
		B	
	R	Y	

- I know there must be a blue in that column.
- There are only two squares available in that column.
- The other square can't be blue because there is already a blue in that row.

This ? must be green

	B	G	Y
G	Y	R	B
	?	B	
	R	Y	

- It is the only square left in the column and the column must contain a green.

This ? must be red

?	B	G	Y
G	Y	R	B
	G	B	
	R	Y	

- It is the only square left in the mini-grid and the mini-grid must contain a red.

This ? must be yellow

R	B	G	Y
G	Y	R	B
?	G	B	
	R	Y	

- I know there must be a yellow in that column.
- There are only two squares available in that column.
- The other square can't be yellow because there is already a yellow in that row.

This ? must be red

R	B	G	Y
G	Y	R	B
Y	G	B	?
	R	Y	

• It is the only square left in the row and the row must contain a red.

This ? must be green

R	B	G	Y
G	Y	R	B
Y	G	B	R
	R	Y	?

• It is the only square left in the column and the column must contain a green.

This ? must be blue

R	B	G	Y
G	Y	R	B
Y	G	B	R
	R	Y	G

• It is the only square left in the mini-grid and the mini-grid must contain a blue.

A further strategy for a 6 x 6 grid

Note that the capital letters stand for the colours Green, Red, Orange, Blue, Yellow, Pink.

The lower case letters are used to reference specific squares.

In the grid there are four squares containing a green (G). It is a useful strategy to try and fill in the other two squares which contain a green. One way of reasoning is as follows:

		G	O		
R					G
	Y			P	
	G			B	
G			a	b	P
		B	R	c	d

Looking at the mini-grid in the bottom right hand corner:

- There must be a green in that mini-grid.
- It can't be in square a or b because there is already a green in that row.
- It can't be in square d because there is already a green in that column.
- **Therefore c must be green.**

		G	O		
R					G
	Y		e	P	g
	G		f	B	h
G					P
		B	R	G	

Looking at the mini-grid on the right hand side in the middle:

- There must be a green in that mini-grid.
- It can't be g or h because there is already a green in that column.
- It can't be f because there is already a green in that row.
- **Therefore e must be green**

SECTION 3: PLONKA BOARDS

Small whiteboards can often be a useful way of providing teachers with immediate feedback but it is possible for them to be overused. Plonka Boards enable children to give their answers in a different way. In response to questions children either put a counter on the answer or plonk their finger on the solution – hence the name. The boards can be photocopied onto paper, or card if they are to be used regularly.

There are six different Plonka Boards with questions for each of them. The questions are loosely arranged for year groups. They are best used with children sitting at tables and can be used by individuals or pairs. As the teacher walks around the classroom the answers given by all children can be seen.

Some questions require an immediate response, but others are examples of 'hover questions'. Children are required to hover over the answer for a hover question and plonk their finger on the answer after 'three, two, one …'. (This results in a very satisfying thud!) Hover questions tend to 'home in' on the solution with several clues. Leave 10 seconds between the first part and the second part of the clue telling children that there may be more than one possibility for the first part, but that the following part or parts of the clue will narrow down the possible solutions. This allows children time to explore possible solutions.

Plonka Boards can also be used by children working together making up the questions for each other and checking solutions.

Time 1

Years 1 – 2

- ... an o'clock time
- ... a half past time
- ... a quarter to time
- ... a quarter past time
- ... a time that is a quarter of an hour before 7 o'clock
- ... a time that is half an hour after 5 o'clock
- ... a time that is quarter of an hour after 2 o'clock
- I am about to eat my lunch. Show me a clock that might be showing the right time.
- Which of the clocks is the nearest to your bed time?

Years 3 - 4

- ... a clock that is showing 11:15
- ... a clock showing 5:30
- ... a clock showing 6:45
- ... a clock showing half an hour after half past 3
- ... a clock showing three quarters of an hour after 7:15
- My watch is half an hour slow. It is really half past three, Show the time on my watch
- My watch is 15 minutes fast. It is really quarter past twelve, Show the time on my watch
- I started playing on the computer at 3:00 and have been playing for an hour and a quarter. What time is it now?

Hover questions

- ... a time which is a 'past' time, ... which starts with 'half' ... which is 30 minutes later than 8 o'clock
- ... a time which is an o'clock time, ... which might be the time when I eat my breakfast
- ... a time which starts with a quarter, ... which is a 'to' time, ... which is 45 minutes after 6 o'clock

Time 1

Time 2

Years 3 - 4

Show me

- … a clock showing ten to eight
- … a clock showing 25 past 1
- … a clock showing 20 to 10
- … a clock showing 5 past 7
- … a clock showing 5:45
- … a clock showing 10:35
- … a clock showing 7:05
- … a clock showing 6:40
- … a clock showing 20 past 12
- … a clock showing five to three
- … a clock showing a time that is 15 minutes later than 10 past 1?
- … a clock showing a time that is an hour earlier than 10 past 6?
- … a clock showing a time that is 45 minutes later than 5:55?
- … a clock showing a time that is 15 minutes earlier than 10 to 11?

Years 5 – 6

- My watch is 15 minutes slow. What time does it show when the real time is:

  - 5:25
  - 9:55
  - 6:55
  - 25 to 1
  - 20 to 2
  - 5 past 8

- My watch is 20 minutes fast. What time does it show when the real time is:

  - 2:25
  - 1:05
  - 6:45
  - 20 past 6
  - Five to 2
  - Half past 7

- My watch is 30 minutes slow. What is the real time when my watch shows:

  - 8:05
  - 12:55
  - 6:35
  - 10 past 6
  - 10 to 12
  - 5 to 1

- My watch is 10 minutes fast. What is the real time when my watch shows:

  - 25 to 2
  - 5 to 6
  - 20 to 6
  - 7:15
  - 2:30
  - 10:45

Hover questions

Show me

- … a time which is a 'past' time, … which starts with 'twenty' … which is between 1 o'clock and 3 o'clock
- … a time which is a 25 time, … which is a 'to' time, … which is a time when many children will be travelling to school
- … a time which is 10 minutes away from an o'clock time, … which has a 50 if written in digital form

Time 2

ATM *It Makes You Think*   © Jill Mansergh 2007   Association of Teachers of Mathematics

Quadrilaterals

Years 5 – 6

Show me

- ... a square
- ... a rhombus
- ... a trapezium
- ... a kite
- ... a rectangle
- ... a parallelogram
- ... a concave quadrilateral
- ... a shape with just one line of symmetry
- ... a shape with exactly two lines of symmetry
- ... a shape with four lines of symmetry

Hover questions

Show me

- ... a shape with one line of symmetry ... with just one pair of parallel sides
- ... a quadrilateral which has no lines of symmetry, ... which has a right angle
- ... a quadrilateral which has four right angles, ... with four equal sides
- ... a quadrilateral which has exactly two lines of symmetry, ... with four equal sides
- ... a quadrilateral which has one line of symmetry, ... with a reflex angle
- ... a quadrilateral which has no equal sides, ... with no parallel sides
- ... a quadrilateral which has exactly one line of symmetry, ... with 3 obtuse angles

Quadrilaterals

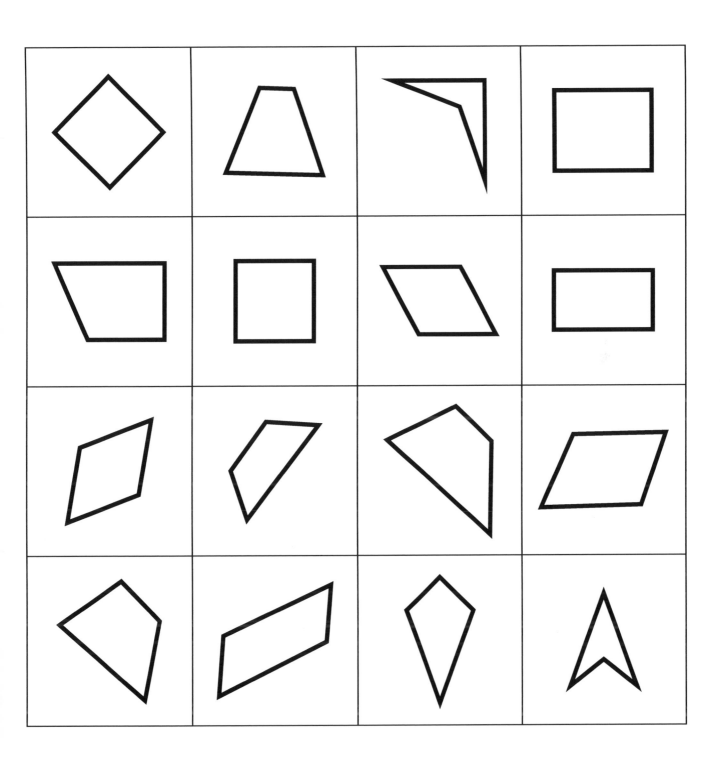

Triangles

Years 3 - 4

Show me

- ... a triangle which has a right angle
- ... a triangle which has an angle that is bigger than a right angle
- ... a triangle which has exactly two equal sides
- ... a triangle which has exactly two equal angles
- ... a triangle which has three equal sides
- ... a triangle which has two equal sides AND a right angle

Years 5 – 6

Show me

- ... a triangle which is isosceles
- ... a triangle which is equilateral
- ... an obtuse angled triangle
- ... a right angled triangle
- ... a right angled triangle which is also isosceles
- ... a triangle which has just one line of symmetry
- ... a triangle which has a vertical line of symmetry

Hover questions

Show me

- ... a triangle which is isosceles, ...which does not have a vertical line of symmetry, ...which does not have a right angle
- ... a triangle which has line symmetry, ... which is equilateral, ... where the sides are not parallel to one of the grid lines
- ... a triangle which does not have line symmetry, ... which has an obtuse angle.

Triangles

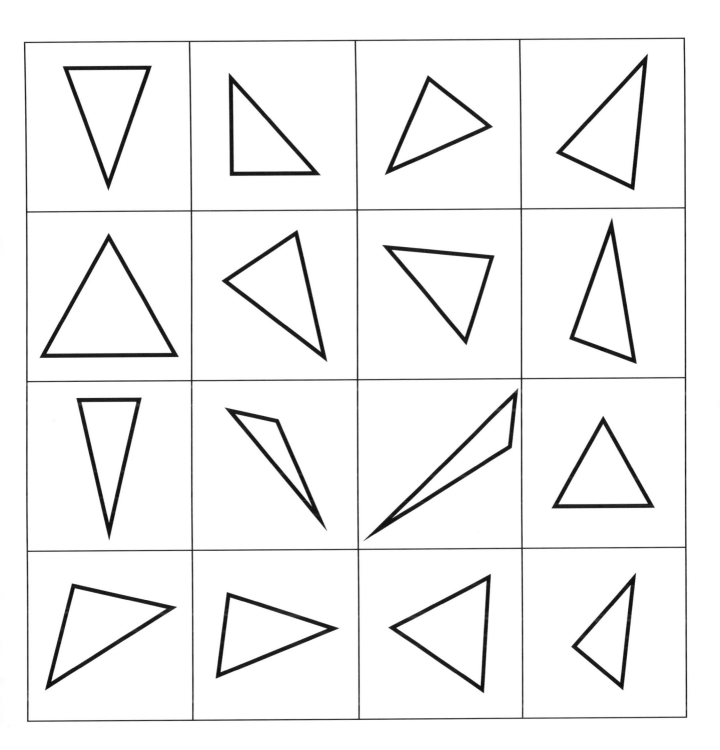

Polygons

Years 1 – 2

Show me

- ... a shape which is called a rectangle
- ... a circle
- ... a shape which has five sides that are all equal
- ... a shape which has five sides that are not all equal
- ... a shape which has at least 2 right angles
- ... a shape which has 12 sides
- ... a shape which has no straight sides

Years 3 - 4

Show me

- ... a right angled triangle
- ... a shape which has five angles
- ... a shape which has five sides AND at least two right angles
- ... a shape which has five sides and a vertical line of symmetry
- ... a shape which has the most right angles
- ... a shape with a horizontal line of symmetry

Years 5 – 6

Show me

- ... a regular pentagon
- ... an irregular pentagon
- ... a hexagon which has only one line of symmetry
- ... a pentagon with just one line of symmetry – and another
- ... a shape which has a right angle AND is also a hexagon
- ... a shape which has a vertical line of symmetry AND more sides than a hexagon
- ... a shape which has two lines of symmetry AND two pairs of parallel sides
- ... a shape which has rotational symmetry order five
- ... a shape which has an infinite number of lines of symmetry

Hover questions

Show me

- ... a shape which has four lines of symmetry, ... which is a regular shape, ... that does not have a line of symmetry which is parallel to one of the grid lines
- ... a quadrilateral, ... which has some right angles, ... which has an obtuse angle
- ... a triangle, ... which is isosceles, ... which is equilateral
- ... a pentagon, .. with one line of symmetry, ... with a horizontal line of symmetry.

Polygons

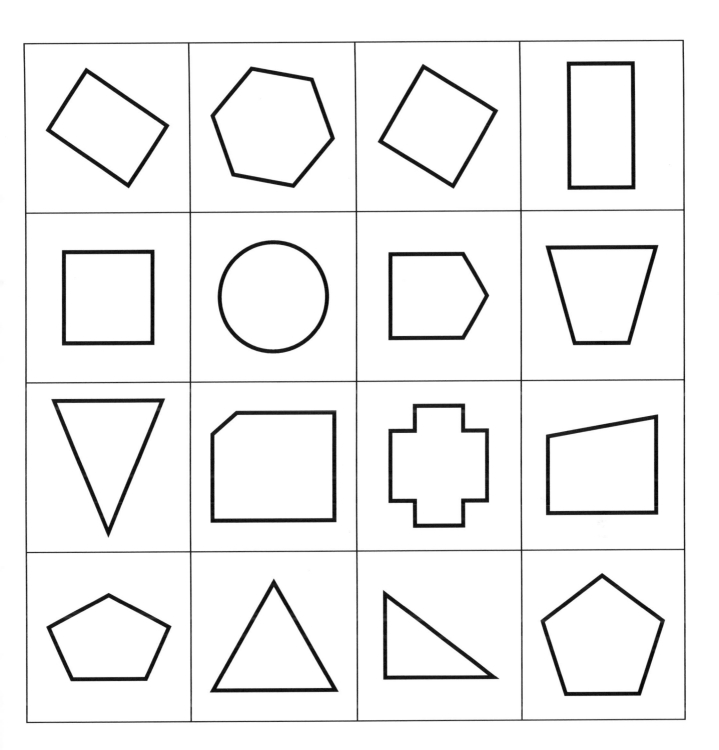

Directions

Year 1 – 2

Show me

- … an arrow pointing up the page
- … an arrow pointing down the page
- … an arrow pointing to the right (or to something specific in the room)
- … an arrow pointing to the left

Year 3 – 4

Show me

- North East
- East
- South
- West
- North West

Year 5 – 6

Show me

- I'm facing North – where is my back facing?
- I'm facing South East and then turn half a turn anti-clockwise
- I'm facing West and then turn a quarter of a turn clockwise
- I'm facing North West where would I be facing after 2.5 turns clockwise?

Hover questions

Show me the way I'm facing when

- I'm facing N, I turn a half turn clockwise, … I turn a quarter of a turn clockwise … I turn 1.5 turns clockwise
- I'm facing SE, … I turn a half turn clockwise, … I turn three quarters of a turn clockwise, … I turn a quarter turn anti-clockwise
- I'm facing NW, … I turn 45° clockwise, … I turn 180° anti-clockwise, .. I turn 45° clockwise

Directions

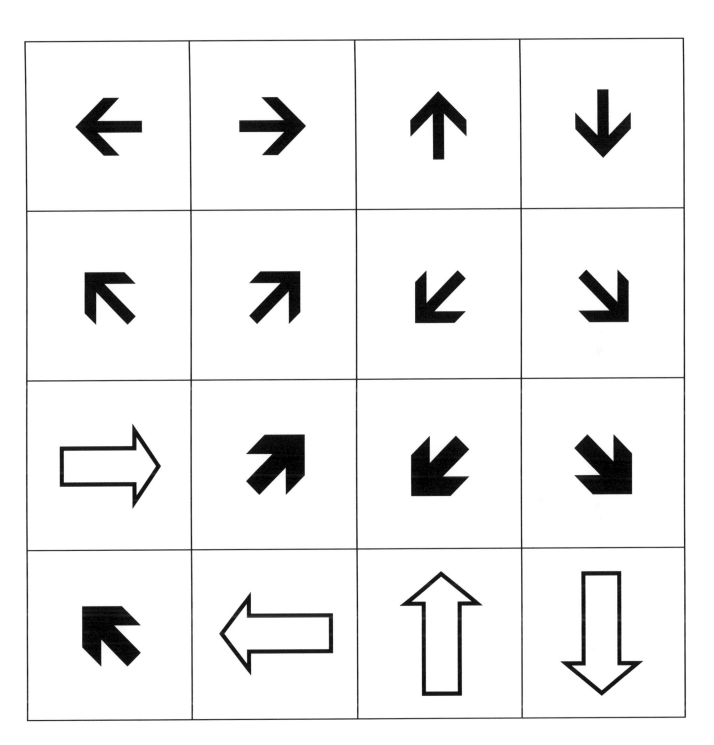

N

SECTION 4: CLUED UP

Clued up is a series of collaborative problem solving activities. The activities develop both individual and group problem solving skills in interesting and meaningful contexts.

Each activity is presented as a series of clues on sets of Clue Cards. Additional Resource Cards to accompany each set of Clue Cards are available on the CD-ROM. The problem to be solved is included in the cards together with sufficient information to find the solution. Some information is included which is irrelevant. The resource cards which are used to solve the problem help to support both visual and kinaesthetic learners.

The activities are arranged in ascending order of difficulty. The first two, Shapes and Colours, are very similar and they have been used successfully with children in key stage 1. Start by working through Colours with the whole class, with children holding colours and moving to the right place. It is also useful for children to hold large versions of the clue cards. When the Colours clues have been solved with the whole class, children work in smaller groups to work through Shapes. A4 versions of the Colours 1 Clue cards can be printed from the CD-ROM.

Many of the later activities are suitable for cross-curricular work.

Instructions for use.

- Children should be organised in groups of 2 – 4 to solve the problem.
- Groups can all work on the same problem or on different problems.
- The title card gives the number of clue cards (excluding the title card) in the set. Before starting children should be encouraged to check that their set is complete.
- Within the set of clue cards is a card saying which other resources should be used.
- The children should be instructed to read all the cards before they start to solve the problem.

Skills used in solving the problem.

In order to solve the problem children may do some or all of the following:

- Read and make sense of the problem
- Ascertain exactly what they are being asked to do
- Sort the cards into categories for solving certain parts of the problem
- Finding the parts of the problem that they can solve
- Solve the problem in stages
- Go back through the information to ensure that all conditions are satisfied

Support with differentiation

These activities can be used with the whole class doing the same activity, or groups working on different activities. Support can be given at different levels. Some children find the labelling of the rows and columns a challenge and might be encouraged to make name labels for them. Alternatively row and column labels can be printed from the CD-Rom for children to use.

You may wish to encourage the children to:

- Check they have the right number of clue cards and resources (written on the title card)
- Read all the clue cards and find the card which tells them what to do
- Solve the problem and check their solution works.

Possible solutions

Children should not need answers to these problems. Some possible solutions are provided for teacher reference at the end of this book.

Colours 1

Groups need: 9 Clue cards 8 Colour cards

You need a set of 8 Colour cards.

Arrange the cards with a space in the middle.

Two of the colours on the top row have 6 letters.

All the colours on the bottom row have 5 letters.

The colours in the middle row have four letters.

Yellow is in the top left hand corner.

Pink is between red and white.

Green is to the right of black.

Blue is above black and below yellow.

Colours 2

Groups need: 9 Clue cards 8 Colour cards

ATM
Association of Teachers of Mathematics

You need a set of 8 Colour cards.

Colours 2

You will not need the red, yellow or blue cards. These are the primary colours.

Colours 2

```
┌──┬──┬──┬──┬──┐
│  │  │  │  │  │
└──┴──┴──┴──┴──┘
 1  2  3  4  5
```

Use the clues to arrange the cards in a row like this.

Colours 2

Pink is beside white.

Colours 2

Green is to the right of black.

Colours 2

The three cards in the middle have 5 letters.

Colours 2

The colour with the longest name is in position number 5.

Colours 2

Black is not next to orange.

Colours 2

Pink is not next to black.

Colours 2

CUT OUT

Colours 3

Groups need: 9 Clue cards 8 Colour cards

You need a set of 8 Colour cards.

Colours 2

Arrange the colour cards in a row following the instructions written on these cards.

Colours 2

The primary colours are in position numbers 1, 2 and 8.

Colours 2

Mixing blue and yellow will give you the colour in position number 6.

Colours 2

Mixing the colours in positions 1 and 8 give orange which is in position 7.

Colours 2

Mixing white which is in position number 3 with position 1 gives the colour in position 5.

Colours 2

The positions of the shapes in the row are numbered 1 to 8 from left to right.

Colours 2

Black is between white and pink

Colours 2

1	2	3	4	5	6	7	8

The cards will look like this when you have arranged them.

Colours 2

CUT OUT

Shapes 1

Groups need: 8 Clue cards 8 Colour cards

You need a set of 8 Shape cards.

Arrange the cards with a space in the middle.

The three sided shapes are in the top corners.

The four sided shapes are in the bottom corners.

The hexagon is to the right of the triangle with three equal sides.

The pentagon is to the left of the shape with four equal sides.

The circle is above the square.

CUT OUT

The octagon is opposite the circle.

Shapes 2

Groups need: 9 Clue cards 8 Colour cards

ATM

You need a set of 8 Shape cards.

ATM

Find all the shapes with 3, 4 or 5 sides.

ATM

---

1 2 3 4 5

Use the clues to arrange the cards in a row like this.

ATM

The pentagon is in the middle of the row.

ATM

The triangle with the right angle is next to the square.

ATM

The triangle with three equal sides is in position number 1.

ATM

The shapes in positions 2 and 4 do not have all the same length sides.

ATM

The triangles are not next to each other.

ATM

The four sided shapes are not next to each other.

ATM

CUT OUT

Shapes 3

Groups need: 9 Clue cards 8 Colour cards

You need a set of 8 Shape cards.

Shapes 3

Arrange the shape cards in a row following the instructions on these cards.

Shapes 3

There is a triangle at the beginning and end of the row.

Shapes 3

The pentagon is between the rectangle and the octagon.

Shapes 3

The square is between the hexagon and the octagon.

Shapes 3

The circle is to the right of a six-sided shape.

Shapes 3

The positions of the shapes in the row are numbered 1 to 8 from left to right.

Shapes 3

The shapes in positions 2, 5 and 8 have right angles.

Shapes 3

1	2	3	4	5	6	7	8

The cards will look like this when you have arranged them.

Shapes 3

UK Flags 1

Groups need: 13 Clue cards Set of Flag cards

ATM
Association of Teachers of Mathematics

The flags are arranged in an array with two rows.

ATM
Association of Teachers of Mathematics

The rows are numbered from the bottom up and the columns from left to right.

ATM
Association of Teachers of Mathematics

There is a flag with the colour blue in both rows.

ATM
Association of Teachers of Mathematics

The flags with the colour blue are not in the same column.

ATM
Association of Teachers of Mathematics

The two flags in column 2 have a vertical line of symmetry.

ATM
Association of Teachers of Mathematics

The colour yellow appears only in column 3.

ATM
Association of Teachers of Mathematics

Two flags in row one have a horizontal line of symmetry.

ATM
Association of Teachers of Mathematics

The flag with a symbol that has rotational symmetry order 3 is in row 2.

ATM
Association of Teachers of Mathematics

The Orkney flag is below the Isle of Man flag.

ATM
Association of Teachers of Mathematics

CUT OUT

The Shetland flag is to the left of the flag of England.

UK Flags 1

ATM
Association of Teachers of Mathematics

The national flag of Wales is known as the Red Dragon.

UK Flags 1

ATM
Association of Teachers of Mathematics

The Scotland flag is to the right of the flag of Wales.

UK Flags 1

ATM
Association of Teachers of Mathematics

You need six UK Flags cards.

UK Flags 1

ATM
Association of Teachers of Mathematics

CUT OUT

UK Flags 2

Groups need: 13 Clue cards Set of Flag cards

ATM

The flags are arranged in a row.

ATM

The positions of the flags are numbered from 1 to 6 from left to right.

ATM

The Isle of Man flag is between the flags with the colour blue.

ATM

The English flag is beside the flag of Scotland.

ATM

The flags with the letter k in their principal town are not next to each other.

ATM

The Red Dragon is in position number 1.

ATM

The English flag is to the right of the flag with a cross on a yellow background.

ATM

The Orkney Islands are off the coast of Scotland.

ATM

The Scottish flag is the flag of St Andrew.

ATM

CUT OUT

The United Kingdom is made up of England, Northern Ireland, Scotland and Wales.

ATM
Association of Teachers of Mathematics

The flag of Shetland is in position number 6.

ATM
Association of Teachers of Mathematics

St George is the patron saint of England.

ATM
Association of Teachers of Mathematics

You need 6 UK Flags cards.

ATM
Association of Teachers of Mathematics

CUT OUT

Animal Watch

Groups need: 18 Clue cards 7 Animal cards

Animal Watch — ATM

Ben spent every evening watching for animals for a week.

Animal Watch — ATM

He started his animal watch on Sunday evening.

Animal Watch — ATM

Work out which animal Ben saw on each evening.

Animal Watch — ATM

Ben did not have to go to school the day after he saw the squirrel.

Animal Watch — ATM

Ben attends school on weekdays, but never at weekends.

Animal Watch — ATM

He saw the fox two days after he saw the badger.

Animal Watch — ATM

He had already seen six other animals when he eventually spotted an otter.

Animal Watch — ATM

Ben saw the hare after he had seen the rabbit, but before he saw the deer.

Animal Watch — ATM

Ben saw the fox on the middle day of his watch.

Animal Watch — ATM

Otters feed mainly on fish, supplemented by frogs, crayfish and crabs.

Animal Watch — ATM

Otters have become rare because of the loss of their natural habitat.

Animal Watch — ATM

Hares can run at speeds of up to 45 mph.

Animal Watch — ATM

Rabbits have young that are born blind and hairless.

Animal Watch — ATM

Hares are generally bigger than rabbits, have longer ears and have black markings on their fur.

Animal Watch — ATM

Badgers are the largest indigenous carnivores in the United Kingdom.

Animal Watch — ATM

Ben saw a different animal on each day.

Animal Watch — ATM

Hedgehogs hibernate during the winter.

Animal Watch — ATM

CUT OUT

You need 7 Animal Watch cards.

Animal Watch — ATM

Faces

Groups need: 13 Clue cards 12 Faces cards

The cards are arranged in an array with three rows.

The rows are numbered from the bottom up and the columns from left to right.

The faces with spectacles are in column 3.

The faces at the base of columns 1 and 2 have symmetrical features.

The face at the top of column 2 has symmetrical features.

The teeth and tongue can be seen in row 3.

There is only one face with symmetrical features in column 1.

Five eyes can be seen in row 2.

The face with a tear is in between the lilac face and the sleeping face.

The face with a heart is directly below the face with a finger in its mouth.

The face with its thumb in its mouth is beside the face with a winking eye.

Five open eyes can be seen in column 1.

You need 12 Faces cards.

CUT OUT

Dinosaurs

Groups need: 17 Clue cards 8 Dinosaur cards
Optional: 8 Time cards

ATM
Association of Teachers of Mathematics

Tyrannosaurus Rex was one of the largest land carnivores of all time. It was about 12 to 13m long and 4.5 to 5m tall.

Dinosaurs — ATM

The dinosaurs went to the lake for a breakfast drink.

Dinosaurs — ATM

At what time did each dinosaur arrive for their breakfast drink?

Dinosaurs — ATM

By the time the Megalosaurus arrived at 07:10 half the dinosaurs had not yet been for their breakfast drink.

Dinosaurs — ATM

The Ceratosaurus went for his drink 40 minutes before the Iguanodon.

Dinosaurs — ATM

There was an arrival at 07:20, with other dinosaurs dining a quarter of an hour earlier and 20 minutes later.

Dinosaurs — ATM

Eight specimens of Archaeopteryx have been found (7 actual specimens and one feather).

Dinosaurs — ATM

The first dinosaur arrived at 06:30, 25 minutes before the Hesperornis strolled in for breakfast.

Dinosaurs — ATM

The last arrival was 1 hour and 20 minutes later than the first and just 5 minutes after the penultimate arrival.

Dinosaurs — ATM

The Stegosaurus drank his fill 10 minutes later than the Brontosaurus.

Dinosaurs — ATM

The Diplodocus arrived later than the Triceratops, but earlier than the Iguanodon.

Dinosaurs — ATM

Giganotosaurus was larger than Tyrannosaurus Rex but had a smaller brain that was the size and shape of a banana.

Dinosaurs — ATM

Dinosaurs first appeared approximately 230 million years ago.

Dinosaurs — ATM

Dinosaurs became extinct approximately 65 million years ago.

Dinosaurs — ATM

The tallest and heaviest dinosaur known from good skeletons is Brachiosaurus Brancai.

Dinosaurs — ATM

The longest complete dinosaur is the 27 m long Diplodocus, which was discovered in Wyoming in the United States.

Dinosaurs — ATM

You need 8 Dinosaur cards.

Dinosaurs — ATM

CUT OUT

Scientists

Groups need: 19 Clue cards 8 Inventor cards
8 Invention cards

ATM

You need 8 Scientist cards and 8 cards showing their inventions.

— Scientists — ATM

Firstly you need to work out which scientist was responsible for each invention.

— Scientists — ATM

Secondly you need to work out where their portraits are displayed on the wall.

— Scientists — ATM

The inventor of the first steamship lived the shortest life.

— Scientists — ATM

The inventors of the telephone and the light bulb were born in the same year.

— Scientists — ATM

The inventors of the steam ship and the cotton gin were born in the same year.

— Scientists — ATM

The inventors of the motor car and the light bulb lived longer than the other scientists.

— Scientists — ATM

The inventor of the telegraph is better known for inventing Morse Code which bears his name.

— Scientists — ATM

The engine still bears the name of its inventor.

— Scientists — ATM

CUT OUT

The pictures are arranged on the wall in two rows of four.

ATM

The inventors born in the 18th century are all in the top row.

ATM

The inventor of the light bulb is between Rudolph Diesel and the inventor of the telephone.

ATM

The scientist in the top right hand corner died in the 20th century when he was in his sixties.

ATM

The pictures of the scientists who were born in the same year are displayed next to each other.

ATM

The picture of the inventor of the telegraph is directly above Henry Ford.

ATM

The picture of Eli Whitney is directly above that of Thomas Edison.

ATM

Robert Fulton's picture is directly to the right of that of Samuel Morse.

ATM

Henry Ford's picture is in a corner.

ATM

The radio inventor is pictured directly above Rudolf Diesel.

ATM

CUT OUT

Explorers

Groups need: 18 Clue cards 8 Explorer cards
8 Explorer Country cards

You need 8 Explorer cards and 8 cards showing the places where they travelled.

You need to arrange the cards in 4 rows with the explorer placed directly above the place he explored.

The rows are numbered 1 - 4 from the bottom upwards, and the columns from left to right.

Row 4 and row 2 have the names of the explorers.

The explorers who went to Antarctica and the South Pole were born in the same year.

The explorer who lived the longest was the first European to visit China.

The explorer who had the shortest life sailed around the world.

The explorer who was born in 1813 discovered the Victoria Falls.

The explorer who reached the North Pole did so in 1909.

The explorer who reached the South Pole lived longer than the explorer who travelled to Antarctica.

ATM

The explorer born in the 15th century is in row 4 and column 4.

ATM

The circumnavigation of the earth, Amundsen and China form a diagonal line.

ATM

Livingstone is between Cook and Shackleton.

ATM

New Zealand, Marco Polo and the South Pole form a diagonal line.

ATM

Dampier travelled extensively and went to the Gulf of Mexico whilst still a teenager.

ATM

Shackleton, the Victoria Falls and Peary form a diagonal line.

ATM

Shackleton was born in Ireland. He was involved in several unsuccessful expeditions to the South Pole.

ATM

CUT OUT

David Livingstone was the first European to cross the width of southern Africa.

ATM

19th Century Novels

Groups need: 19 Clue cards 8 Author cards
8 Book cards

There are two parts
to this problem.

Firstly you need to work
out which author wrote
each book.

The second part of the
problem is to arrange the
cards in the way that the
books were placed on the
table.

Eight books written in the
19th century are placed
evenly spaced around an
octagonal table.

The book by Mark Twain
was next to the book by
Jane Austin.

You need to place the book
card and its author card as
if they were on the table.

The cards show pictures of
books with the date they
were first published, and
the authors of those books.

Jane Austen was the first of
the authors to have a book
published.

Hans Christian Anderson's
book was first published
11 years before Charlotte
Bronte's book.

CUT OUT

Rudyard Kipling, Mark Twain, Hans Christian Anderson and Thomas Hardy published in even numbered years.

ATM

Mark Twain and Hans Christian Anderson published in years that are divisible by 3.

ATM

Rudyard Kipling's book was published 20 years after the one written by Thomas Hardy.

ATM

Lewis Carroll published his book 18 years after Charlotte Brontë.

ATM

You need 8 author cards and 8 cards showing the names of the books they have written.

ATM

If the table was a clock face, Thomas Hardy was placed at 12 o'clock.

ATM

The two female authors were placed next to each other.

ATM

The date of publication of the book at quarter past had three even numbered digits.

ATM

Lewis Carroll was placed opposite Rudyard Kipling.

ATM

Hans Christian Anderson had Robert Louis Stevenson on his left and Lewis Carroll on his right.

ATM

Music Composers

Groups need: 24 Clue cards 8 Composer cards
8 Composition cards
8 Country cards

You need 8 Composer cards, 8 Composition cards and 8 Country cards.

Music Composers

To solve the problem you need to match the composer to their country of birth and their composition.

Music Composers

To solve the problem you need to arrange the cards in three rows.

Music Composers

The top row will show the composer's name and the middle row will show their country of birth.

Music Composers

The bottom row will show the compositions.

Music Composers

The problem involves 8 great musical composers, their country of birth and a famous piece of music they composed.

Music Composers

The composer, his country of birth and one of his famous compositions will appear in the same column.

Music Composers

Arrange the 24 cards according to the clues given.

Music Composers

The columns are labelled 1 – 8 from left to right.

Music Composers

CUT OUT

The rows are labelled top, middle and bottom.

The composer who was born second is in column 4.

The composers in columns 1, 3 and 8 only have two names.

Vivaldi is between Tchaikovsky and Mozart.

The composer in column 3 was born the year before the composer in column 1.

The three composers whose year of birth was a multiple of 10 are in columns 2, 3 and 7.

Madame Butterfly is an opera written by an Italian composer.

A Little Night Music is a name sometimes given to Mozart's Eine Kleine Nachtmusik.

Liszt who composed the Hungarian Rhapsodies is considered one of the greatest pianists of all time.

The compositions with a number in the title are in columns 6 and 7.

Bach, Austria and The Four Seasons form a diagonal line.

Germany is between Poland and Hungary, and also between Poland and Austria.

The composer of the Minute Waltz was not born in Germany.

Beethoven composed the Sonata.

CUT OUT

The composers who were born in the same country are not placed next to each other.

POSSIBLE SOLUTIONS

Shaping up

3x3 Crazy Square

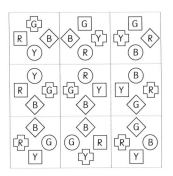

4x4 Crazy Square

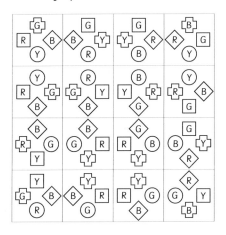

Clued up

Colours 1

Yellow	Orange	Red
Blue		Pink
Black	Green	White

Colours 2

Pink	White	Black	Green	Orange

Colours 3

Red	Blue	White	Black	Pink	Green	Orange	Yellow

Shapes 1

Equilateral Triangle	Hexagon	Triangle
Octagon		Circle
Rectangle	Pentagon	Square

Shapes 2

Equilateral Triangle	Rectangle	Pentagon	Triangle	Square

Shapes 3

Equilateral Triangle	Rectangle	Pentagon	Octagon	Square	Hexagon	Circle	Triangle

Flags 1

Shetland	England	Isle of Man
Wales	Scotland	Orkney

Flags 2

Wales	Jersey	England	Scotland	Isle of Man	Shetland

Animal Watch

Sunday	Rabbit
Monday	Badger
Tuesday	Hare
Wednesday	Fox
Thursday	Deer
Friday	Squirrel
Saturday	Otter

Faces

Dinosaurs

Triceratops	06:30
Hesperornis	06:55
Ceratosaurus	07:05
Megalosaurus	07:06
Diplodocus	07:21
Brontosaurus	07:40
Iguanodon	07:45
Stegosaurus	07:50

SCIENTISTS AND INVENTIONS

Scientist	Inventions
Alexander Graham Bell	Telephone
Thomas Edison	Light Bulb
Eli Whitney	Cotton Ginn
Guglielmo Marconi	Radio
Henry Ford	Motor Car
Robert Fulton	Steam ship
Samuel Morse	Telegraph
Rudolf Diesel	Diesel Engine

Scientist Picture Gallery

Samuel Morse	Robert Fulton	Eli Whitney	Guglielmo Marconi
Henry Ford	Alexander Graham Bell	Thomas Edison	Rudolf Diesel

Explorers

Captain James Cook (1728-1779)	David Livingstone (1813 - 1873)	Ernest Shackleton (1872-1922)	Ferdinand Magellan (1480-1521)
New Zealand	Victoria Falls	Antarctica	Circumnavigation of Earth
Robert Edwin Peary (1856 - 1920)	Marco Polo (1254-1324)	Roald Amundsen (1872-1928)	William Dampier (1652-1715)
North Pole	China	South Pole	Gulf of Mexico

19th Century Novels

Author	Book
Jane Austin	Pride and Prejudice
Hans Christian Anderson	The Little Mermaid
Charlotte Brontë	Jane Eyre
Lewis Carroll	Alice's Adventures in Wonderland
Thomas Hardy	Far from the Madding Crowd
Robert Louis Stevenson	Treasure Island
Mark Twain	The Adventures of Huckleberry Finn
Rudyard Kipling	Jungle Book

Table Positions

Thomas Hardy

Robert Louis Stevenson   Rudyard Kipling

Hans Christian Anderson   Mark Twain

Lewis Carol   Jane Austin

Charlotte Brontë

Music Composers

Franz Lizst	Ludwig van Beethoven	Frederic Chopin	Johann Sebastian Bach	Wolfgang Amedeus Mozart	Antonio Lucio Vivaldi	Piortr Ilyitch Tchaikovsky	Giacomo Puccini
Hungary	Germany	Poland	Germany	Austria	Italy	Russia	Italy
Hungarian Rhapsodies	Moonlight Sonata	Minute Waltz	Brandenburg Concerto	A Little Night Music	The Four Seasons	1812 Overture	Madam Butterfly

Resources on the CD-Rom

SECTION 1	SHAPING UP	
	Shape Cards 1	
	Shape Cards 2	
	Shape Cards 3	
	Shape Cards 4	
	Shape Cards 5	
	Blank shape cards	
SECTION 2	COLOUR SUDOKU	
	4 x 4 Colour Sudoku	
	6 x 6 Colour Sudoku	
SECTION 3	PLONKA BOARDS	
	Time 1	
	Time 2	
	Quadrilaterals	
	Triangles	
	Polygons	
	Directions	
SECTION 4	CLUED UP	
	Colours 1	Clue cards
	Colours 2	Clue cards
	Colours 3	Clue cards
	Colour cards	A4 size
	Colours 1 Clue cards	A4 size
	Shapes 1	Clue cards
	Shapes 2	Clue cards
	Shapes 3	Clue cards
		Shapes cards
	UK Flags 1	Clue cards
	UK Flags 2	Clue cards
		Flags cards
	Animal Watch	Clue cards
		Animal Watch cards
	Faces	Clue cards
		Faces cards
	Dinosaurs	Clue cards
		Dinosaur cards
		Time cards
	Scientists	Clue cards
		Inventor cards
		Invention cards
	Explorers	Clue cards
		Explorer cards
		Explorer Country cards
	19th Century Novels	Clue cards
		Author cards
		Book cards
	Music Composers	Clue cards
		Composer cards
		Composition cards
		Composer Country cards
	Row & Column labels	